The
Scarlet
Letter

Nathaniel Haw

Academic Industries, Inc.
West Haven, Connecticut 06516

ISBN 0-88301-719-9

Published by
Academic Industries, Inc.
The Academic Building
Saw Mill Road
West Haven, Connecticut 06516

Printed in the United States of America

ABOUT THE AUTHOR

Nathaniel Hawthorne, an American romance writer, was born in Salem, Massachusetts in 1804. He was educated at Bowdoin College in Maine and was the most distinguished craftsman of the New England school of letters. He led a quiet life, removed from the activities of his times, in a restless solitude. Because of his passionless upbringing, he had a strong pride and sense of alienation from the world in which he lived.

At age forty-five he wrote a story which had long been stored in his mind—*The Scarlet Letter*. At last he found success. Written with intense gloom and great indifference, Hawthorne's restlessness can easily be felt throughout the novel.

Even though Hawthorne's concern is always with what is ethical, only rarely does his imagination join with creative passion. More frequently you will find just a hint of emotion.

Nathaniel Hawthorne
The Scarlet Letter

Arthur Dimmesdale

Roger Chillingworth

Pearl

Hester Prynne

Governor Bellingham

One quiet, rainy day I made a discovery—a small package wrapped in old paper. The object that most caught my attention was a bit of fine red cloth decorated with gold. It was the capital letter A. I happened to place it on my chest. I felt burning heat—as if it were not red cloth, but red-hot iron. I trembled and let it fall to the floor. I examined the papers to find the story that lay behind this strange letter.

On a summer morning in 1642, most of the people of the town of Boston, Massachusetts, were gathered before the jail. It was an angry Puritan crowd. Their eyes were glued to the strong, oaken prison door.

The women seemed to take a special interest.

I think, ladies, it would be better for everybody if we women took care of such sinners as this Hester Prynne!

If this woman stood up for judgment before us five, would she come off with such a sentence as the judges have given? I think not!

The judges are too easy, that is the truth.

At least, they should have marked her forehead with a hot iron!

Why do we talk of marks?

She has brought shame upon us all and ought to die!

Be quiet, women! The door is opening!

The door was flung open. Like a black shadow, the town crier appeared.

He led a young woman toward the door.

The hussy! She uses her skill with the needle to laugh in our faces!

We should strip her gown off her shoulders.

I'll give a piece of my old red flannel to make a more fitting letter. She wears the scarlet letter of a sinner as if it were an honor instead of a curse.

Make way, good people, in the name of the King.

Open a passage, and Mistress Prynne shall be set where man, woman, and child may have a sight of her mark of sin!

Come along, Mistress Hester, and show your scarlet letter in the marketplace!

A lane was opened through the crowd, and Hester Prynne walked towards the place set for her punishment.

Schoolboys ran in front, staring up into her face.

Though every step was torture, she passed through this part of her punishment with outward calm, and reached the marketplace.

Knowing what to do, she climbed a flight of wooden steps.

There she stood for everyone to see. She felt at times, as if she must cry out, and throw herself from the scaffold, or else go mad.

Yet there were times when the whole scene seemed to disappear. She saw, instead, the path along which she had been walking since she was a little girl.

In her mind she saw again the village in which she was born in Old England, and her home: an old, poor house of gray stone, now falling apart.

She saw her father's face. . . .

Her mother's too, with its look of love. . . .

She saw her own face in the mirror in which she had so often looked.

There was another face in her memory—thin and intelligent. He was an older man with his left shoulder higher than his right—a new life seemed to wait for her.

Now she stood here. Could it be true? She held the child until it cried. She looked down at the scarlet letter and touched it. Yes! The baby and the shame were real. All else had disappeared.

To help her forget, she looked over the crowd. On its outer edge, two men caught her eye: an Indian, and beside him a white man dressed in a strange mixture of civilized and savage clothes.

At the sight of the white man, Hester drew back. Her eyes met his across the crowd. He raised his finger and put it to his lips.

Sir, who is this woman? Why, is she set up to public shame?

Friend, you must be a stranger, not to have heard of Mistress Prynne. She has raised a great scandal in Master Dimmesdale's church.

I am a stranger. I have met with sad adventures by sea and land, and have been held captive by the Indians. Will you tell me of this woman's crimes?

Truly, I will, friend. And you must be glad to find yourself here, where sin is searched out and punished!

This woman was the wife of an intelligent Englishman, who was to come over and join us in Massachusetts.

....In the two years she has been here, no word has come of her husband! And the young wife, being left alone....

He sent his wife before him, staying himself to look after some business. But sir, would you believe it....

Aha! I see. So wise a husband should have learned this too in his books! And who is the babe's father?

The husband should come himself to solve the mystery.

That is a riddle! Mistress Prynne refuses to name him.

Most likely he is at the bottom of the sea. That is why our good judges, instead of asking for her death, have only asked that she stand here for three hours—and wear the scarlet letter for the rest of her life.

17

Hester was awakened from her thoughts by a voice.

Listen, Hester Prynne!

It was the voice of John Wilson, the oldest clergyman of Boston.

I have asked my young friend, your pastor, the goodly Mr. Dimmesdale, to deal with you, here before all the people—to get you to tell the name of the man who led you into this sin. He is against it, but I asked him once again!

This appeal drew all eyes to the Reverend Mr. Dimmesdale. Though very intelligent and a fine speaker, he was nervous and shy and liked to avoid attention. He now stepped forward.

Hester Prynne, if you feel it to be for your soul's peace, I charge you to speak out the name of your fellow-sinner and fellow-sufferer! Be not silent from any mistaken pity for him; for believe me, Hester. . . .

. . . .better he step down from a high place to stand beside you, than to hide a guilty heart through life!

Everyone liked the young pastor's sweet, rich voice. Even the baby felt its influence, and held up its little arms toward him.

Even the babe agrees with the advice you have heard. Woman, speak out the name!

Never! I will not speak!

The wonderful woman! She will not speak. She is so strong.

And so, her secret still her own, Hester Prynne was led back to prison.

Returned to prison, Hester was in a state of nervous excitement that could not be calmed.

The baby shared her trouble.

The jailer, afraid she might harm herself or the baby, brought in Dr. Chillingworth.

Now, mistress, here's a doctor who may help you!

Leave me alone with my patient, good jailer.

My studies and my stay with the Indians—they know about herbs and such—have made me a better doctor than most.

Here, woman! Give the babe this medicine.

No! Would you take revenge on an innocent baby?

Foolish woman! The medicine will help the baby. I'll give it myself.

Soon, its pain gone, the baby sank into a healthy sleep.

And now, something for you—a recipe an Indian taught me. It will calm you!

I have thought of death . . .wished for it! Is it in this cup?

Do you know me so little? Even if I plan revenge, what better revenge than to let you live!

No—the reason for your crime is my own foolishness! I, a scholar, already old, crippled from birth—what had I to do with youth and beauty like yours!

I was honest. I never pretended to love you.

True. But I was lonely. It seemed not so wild a dream, to marry and create warmth and love!

I have greatly wronged you.

We have wronged each other. We are even. But the man lives who has wronged us both!

Who is he, Hester?

You shall never know!

22

I mean him no harm. Let him live! Let him hide himself! But I will find him out. Meanwhile, as you keep his secret, keep mine. Tell no one I am your husband.

Why do you ask it?

Perhaps I don't wish to be known as the husband of a sinful woman. For whatever reason, swear to keep my secret!

I swear it!

And now I leave you—alone with your infant, and the scarlet letter—and perhaps your nightmares!

Why do you smile so? Have you led me into a promise that will prove the ruin of my soul?

Not your soul, Hester. No, not yours!

Hester's term in jail came to an end. To her sick heart, it seemed as if the outside sunshine was meant only to show the scarlet letter.

With the permission of the judges, she moved into a lonely cottage on the edge of town.

In this little lonesome house she moved in with her child, little Pearl.

At the art of needlework, Hester was an expert. This skill filled a need in the village by which she could provide an income for herself and Pearl.

One day as Hester bent over the candle, Pearl's eyes were caught by the gold on the letter A. Putting up her little hand, she grabbed it, laughing!

Thus the first object Pearl seemed to notice in her life was the scarlet letter.

As she grew, Pearl had no friends among the little Puritans. She never tried to speak to the other children.

If they gathered around her, as they sometimes did. . . .

She would chase them and throw stones at them.

But at home, she had many games and playmates.

The ugliest weeds of the garden were their children whom she struck down.

The black and solemn pine trees became older Puritans whom she laughed at.

Hester and Pearl went one day, to Governor Bellingham's mansion.

Come, child. Let us deliver to the Governor these decorated gloves he ordered.

But Hester had another reason. She had heard that there were plans to take Pearl away from her, to give her wiser and better care.

Pearl was dressed in a red velvet dress decorated with gold thread. As they came into town, they passed a group of Puritan children.

But Pearl, after stamping her foot and shaking her fist, made a rush at her enemies, and they ran away.

Without further adventure, they reached Governor Bellingham's house.

Is the Governor home?

Yes, but he has visitors. You may not see him now.

Nevertheless, I will enter.

On the wall of the great hall hung a row of pictures. Standing on the floor was a suit of armor, highly polished.

Mother, I see you here. Look! Look!

Hush, child! Come away. The Governor and his guests are coming.

Well! What have we here?

Indeed, what little bird of scarlet is this? Are you a Christian child?

I am mother's child, and my name is Pearl.

But where is your mother? Ah, I see!

This is the child about whom we spoke. . .and her unhappy mother, Hester Prynne!

We might have guessed that her mother must be a scarlet woman! We will look into this matter.

The Governor and his guests entered the hall.

Hester Prynne, there has been much talk about the child. Would it not be for her good if she were taken from you, dressed properly, and taught manners and the truths of heaven and earth?

By a sudden impulse, Hester turned to the young clergyman, Mr. Dimmesdale.

He stepped forward, pale and holding his hand over his heart as was his habit when disturbed.

Speak for me! You were my pastor and know me better than these men can. I will not lose the child! Help me!

There is truth in what she says, and in her feeling. With the child, God gave her a blessing and also a torture. She has expressed this in the dress of the poor child, reminding us of what the red letter stands for.

Well said! I feared she had no better thought than to make a clown of the child.

O, not so! She knows that the child was meant by God to keep the mother's soul alive. For her sake, no less than for the child's, let us leave them as God has placed them.

You speak with a strange interest.

And has he not pleaded well for the poor woman?

So well, indeed, that we will leave the matter as it now stands; so long as there is no further scandal.

In those days everyone believed in witches and wizards, and a devil who was everywhere. Mistress Hibbins, the Governor's bad-tempered sister, was called a witch; and it is said that she leaned from an upper window as Hester left the house.

Hist! Will you go with us tonight? There will be a merry company in the forest, and I promised the Devil that Hester Prynne would be there!

No, I must stay at home and care for my little Pearl. Had they taken her from me, I would gladly have gone with you—and signed my name in the black book, too.

Pearl had saved her mother from the devil's trap, proving what the young minister said was true.

Young Arthur Dimmesdale was loved and admired by his church members. About this time, his health had begun to fail. Each Sunday he was paler and thinner, his voice weaker.

The people looked on Roger Chillingworth as a miracle meant to save their beloved pastor since he had great knowledge in medicine. The church elders arranged for Chillingworth to care for Dimmesdale.

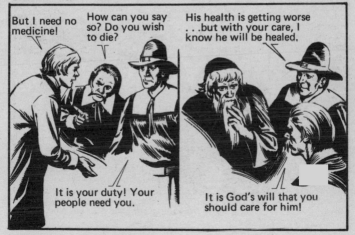

But I need no medicine!

How can you say so? Do you wish to die?

His health is getting worse . . .but with your care, I know he will be healed.

It is your duty! Your people need you.

It is God's will that you should care for him!

It was arranged for them to have a room in the same house, so that the doctor might keep a constant eye on his patient.

Mr. Dimmesdale had a front apartment.

On the other side of the house, Chillingworth arranged his study and laboratory.

But as the years passed, Dimmesdale became more troubled, more ill. He often had visions and nightmares during the night.

Now it was a herd of devilish shapes that grinned and haunted him. . . .

Now a group of shining angels, who unhappily flew upward. . . .

On one such night, dark and cloudy, in early May, Dimmesdale quietly dressed himself and left the house. As if in a dream, he made his way to that same scaffold where Hester Prynne had stood seven years ago.

But the town is asleep—no one can see me—it means nothing.

Suddenly he shouted . . . a cry that went ringing through the night.

The whole town will rush out and find me here!

He covered his face and waited for discovery.

But it was not so. The town did not awake. He opened his eyes and looked around. In Governor Bellingham's house, the governor stood at one window looking out. At another window, Mistress Hibbins stuck out her head.

But they put out their lights and returned to bed again. The minister grew more calm.

> Then he saw a little, flickering light, coming up the street. It was someone carrying a lantern.

It threw a light on a window-pane. . . .

. . . .and than a pump with its water tank. . . .

. . . .and then, coming closer, a door of oak.

It was the Reverend Wilson returning from some errand—and now he would surely look up and see Dimmesdale!

But he passed by and away down the street with never a look upward! Dimmesdale laughed in relief. . .and a light, childish laugh answered him!

Pearl! Little Pearl! Hester? Are you there?

Hester held Pearl by one hand. The minister took the other hand, and felt a rush of life pouring through his veins, as if the three of them formed an electric chain.

Will you stand here with mother and me, tomorrow at noon?

No, my child. Someday, indeed, but not tomorrow!

Pearl laughed and tried to pull away her hand but he held it tight.

A moment longer, my child!

But will you promise to take my hand, and mother's hand, tomorrow at noon?

Not then, Pearl, but another time.

And what other time?

At the great judgment day, we must stand together before God. But not in the daylight of the world!

41

But before he had finished speaking, a light filled the sky, lighting the scene with the clearness of midday—as if it were the daylight that would unite all who belong together. And the meteor —if it were that—shone through the clouds in the shape of a great letter A!

At the time he saw the miraculous letter, Dimmesdale was aware that Pearl was pointing her finger at old Roger Chillingworth standing near.

So real was his impression that, in the deep darkness after the meteor had vanished, Chillingworth's face still seemed painted on the blackness.

Who is that man, Hester? Do you know him? I have a nameless horror of the man!

But Hester remembered her promise and was silent.

Good Master Dimmesdale, can this be you! You dream while awake and walk in your sleep! Come, my friend, let me take you home.

How did you know I was here?

I was at the deathbed of Governor Winthrop. After he died, I was going home. Come with me now, or you will hardly be able to speak tomorrow.

I will go home with you.

So Dimmesdale gave in to the doctor and was led away.

Yet the next day, he gave a talk which was held to be the richest and most powerful he had ever preached. Afterward as he came down the pulpit steps, the church watchman met him.

Your glove, sir. It was found this morning on the scaffold, where evil doers are set up. No doubt the devil dropped it there as a bad joke!

Thank you, my friend. Yes, it seems to be my glove!

Did you hear of the sign that was seen last night? A great red letter in the sky. . . .

The letter A, which we think stands for Angel. As our good Governor Winthrop was made an angel last night, it was fitting that there should be some notice!

No, I had not heard of it.

During the past seven years, Hester's place in the community had changed. By doing her work well, she earned a living for herself and Pearl. She never complained when treated badly.

None was more ready to give to the poor.

Thank you, my child!

When there was illness or trouble, she brought help and comfort.

On the night of their strange meeting, she was shocked at Mr. Dimmesdale's condition. Made strong by her own years of trouble, she felt better able to deal with Roger Chillingworth than on that time long ago in the prison room. She promised herself to talk to her former husband.

One afternoon walking with Pearl, she saw the old doctor looking for roots and herbs.

Run and play on the beach while I talk with the doctor.

I would speak a word with you.

Ah! Is it Mistress Hester that has a word for old Roger Chillingworth?

Once again, Hester was shocked to see the change that had taken place in a man in the past seven years.

What do you see in my face, that you stare so?

Never mind. It is of the minister I would speak.

When we last spoke together, seven years ago, I promised to keep secret that you had been my husband.

What choice had you? My finger pointed at the minister would have thrown him into prison—perhaps even had him hanged!

It would have been better that he died at once than to have his worst enemy, unknown at his side!

Yes, you are right! Never has a man suffered more!

Now, I must tell him, no matter what you do! This way there is no good for him—no good for me, no good for you!

Hester, if you had met me earlier with a better love than mine, this evil would not have happened! I pity you for the good that has been wasted in you!

And I you, for the hatred that has turned a good man to an evil man.

So one day soon after, Hester set out to meet Dimmesdale, who would be returning through the forest from a visit to his Indian converts. When she heard him coming, she sent Pearl to play along the brook.

She called, quietly at first and then louder.

Arthur Dimmesdale! Arthur Dimmesdale!

Hester! Hester Prynne! Is it you?

Have you found peace, Arthur?

Together they moved back into the shadow of the woods and sat on a bank of moss.

None! Nothing but pain. The people honor me, listen to my words, but I am a ruined soul! I should have given up being a minister. Happy are you to wear the scarlet letter openly.

Both understood.

Once they made the decision to leave, they began to make plans. Hester knew the captain of a ship that was to sail for Bristol, England, in three days. Hester would get tickets for Dimmesdale, Pearl, and herself without telling anyone in the town. They would sail the day after Election Day which was a great holiday.

Early on the morning of Election Day, Hester and Pearl came into the marketplace.

What is it, Mother? Why have all the people dressed up and left their work?

It is the day when a new Governor begins his rule. There will be a parade, with music and soldiers.

Will the minister be there? And will he hold out his hands to me?

He will be there, but he will not greet you nor must you greet him!

A party of Indians and a group of sailors added color to the Puritan crowd. Pearl danced about like a butterfly, among them.

As always, people stepped back from Hester Prynne, leaving a sort of magic circle around her. So she was alone when the ship's captain came up to her.

So, mistress, I hear I must get ready one more cabin than you said!

What do you mean? Have you another passenger?

Why you must know! This doctor here—Chillingworth—tells me he is one of your group.

At that moment she saw Chillingworth across the marketplace smiling at her—a smile of secret and fearful meaning.

Before she could think of what to do, she heard the sound of music. The parade was beginning!

After the music and the soldiers came the judges. Then came the young minister, looking tall and stronger than any had seen him before—and at the same time spiritual, withdrawn.

The parade and most of the crowd entered the meetingplace. The minister began his sermon. Hester stood statue-like, at the foot of the scaffold, near enough to hear his voice.

The holy minister in the church— the woman of the scarlet letter in the marketplace! Who could have imagined that the same sin was on them both!

The sermon ended. The people were overcome with its greatness. The parade began to march back to the town hall. But the shouts of the crowd died to murmurs as they saw the minister again. How feeble and pale he looked!

The Reverend Wilson offered his arm. Governor Bellingham hurried to help.

But the minister waved them away. He had stopped beside Hester and little Pearl.

He turned towards the scaffold and stretched out his arms.

Hester, come here! Come, my little Pearl!

The child flew to him and wrapped her arms about his knees. Hester drew slowly near.

Suddenly Chillingworth pushed through the crowd and whispered to him.

Madman, wait! Keep that woman away. You will be ruined.

Devil, you are too late. I will get away from you now.

Come, Hester! Help me reach the scaffold.

The crowd was shocked. Those near the minister were so surprised that they did nothing. They saw the minister, helped by Hester, climb the scaffold steps.

There is no place in the world you could have escaped me, except on this very scaffold!

Isn't this a better escape than we planned? Hester, I am a dying man. Let me hurry to take my shame upon me!

People of New England—you who have loved me and thought me holy—look on a sinner! Look at the letter Hester wears—you have shaken at it!

But one who lived with you wore the scarlet letter hidden. Hester's is just a shadow of his own—God's hidden judgment on a sinner. Look!

With a shaking motion, he tore away the front of his shirt. The letter was seen by everyone.

Then, down he sank upon the scaffold!

You have escaped me! You have escaped me!

Pearl, will you kiss me now?

Pearl kissed him and her tears fell upon her father's cheek.

Hester, farewell!

Won't we meet again? Won't we be together in heaven?

God alone knows; and he is merciful! His will be done! Farewell!

The final word came forth with his dying breath. The crowd broke out in a strange, deep sound of wonder.

After several days had passed, people tried to arrange their thoughts. There were three ideas as to what had been seen on the scaffold.

It seems likely—he did it himself when Hester Prynne first wore her badge of sin!

Did what, then?

Marked himself with a secret letter A!

No, no! I say old Roger Chillingworth caused it to appear, with his magic and his drugs!

Reverend Wilson had a kinder explanation.

For all his sins, he was a good man! It was sorrow, I believe—eating from his heart outward!

Nothing was stranger than the change in Chillingworth, who seemed to dry up. He died within the year, leaving Governor Bellingham and the Reverend Wilson in charge of his will.

We have here Roger Chillingworth's last will and testament.

He has left his money, both here and in England, to little Pearl, daughter of Hester Prynne!

So little Pearl became the richest heiress of her day in New England. If she stayed there, she might later have wed the son of the holiest Puritan among them! But soon after the doctor's death, Hester and Pearl sailed away.

For many years, few reports came from across the sea. The story of the scarlet letter became a legend. In all those years no one went into Hester's home. Then one afternoon, children playing nearby saw a tall woman in a gray robe come up to the cottage door.

She turned for a moment—showing a scarlet letter on her breast!

Hester Prynne had come back to live in New England. But where was little Pearl who must now be a woman. No one learned for sure. But for the rest of her life Hester received letters and other signs of love from someone in another land.

Letters came with the names of rich people on them. In the cottage were things of comfort which only wealth could have brought, and love have thought of. Once, Hester was seen decorating a baby dress of rich cloth.

Everyone believed that Pearl was married, and happy; she would have liked to have her mother live with her. But there was a more real life for Hester Prynne in New England.

People told her their sorrows and worries, and asked her advice—women, especially.

But why? Why must women be so unhappy, so punished, so unfree?

Hester helped them as best she could.

In heaven's own time, a new truth will be seen. The relation between man and woman will be based on a surer ground, of happiness for both!

After many more years, a new grave was dug in the burial-ground, near an old and sunken one. One tombstone served for both.

The only mark on the tombstone was a large red letter "A" on a black background.

COMPLETE LIST OF POCKET CLASSICS AVAILABLE

CLASSICS

C 1 Black Beauty
C 2 The Call of the Wild
C 3 Dr. Jekyll and Mr. Hyde
C 4 Dracula
C 5 Frankenstein
C 6 Huckleberry Finn
C 7 Moby Dick
C 8 The Red Badge of Courage
C 9 The Time Machine
C10 Tom Sawyer
C11 Treasure Island
C12 20,000 Leagues Under the Sea
C13 The Great Adventures of Sherlock Holmes
C14 Gulliver's Travels
C15 The Hunchback of Notre Dame
C16 The Invisible Man
C17 Journey to the Center of the Earth
C18 Kidnapped
C19 The Mysterious Island
C20 The Scarlet Letter
C21 The Story of My Life
C22 A Tale of Two Cities
C23 The Three Musketeers
C24 The War of the Worlds
C25 Around the World in Eighty Days
C26 Captains Courageous
C27 A Connecticut Yankee in King Arthur's Court
C28 The Hound of the Baskervilles
C29 The House of the Seven Gables
C30 Jane Eyre
C31 The Last of the Mohicans
C32 The Best of O. Henry
C33 The Best of Poe
C34 Two Years Before the Mast
C35 White Fang
C36 Wuthering Heights
C37 Ben Hur
C38 A Christmas Carol
C39 The Food of the Gods
C40 Ivanhoe
C41 The Man in the Iron Mask
C42 The Prince and the Pauper
C43 The Prisoner of Zenda
C44 The Return of the Native
C45 Robinson Crusoe
C46 The Scarlet Pimpernel

COMPLETE LIST OF POCKET CLASSICS AVAILABLE
(cont'd)

C47 The Sea Wolf
C48 The Swiss Family Robinson
C49 Billy Budd
C50 Crime and Punishment
C51 Don Quixote
C52 Great Expectations
C53 Heidi
C54 The Illiad
C55 Lord Jim
C56 The Mutiny on Board H.M.S. Bounty
C57 The Odyssey
C58 Oliver Twist
C59 Pride and Prejudice
C60 The Turn of the Screw

SHAKESPEARE

S 1 As You Like It
S 2 Hamlet
S 3 Julius Caesar
S 4 King Lear
S 5 Macbeth
S 6 The Merchant of Venice
S 7 A Midsummer Night's Dream
S 8 Othello
S 9 Romeo and Juliet
S10 The Taming of the Shrew
S11 The Tempest
S12 Twelfth Night